Support for Handwrit

Book 5

Louis Fidge

Illustrated by Chris Hahner

Contents

Name: _____

Remember! There are **four basic joins**.
Here is an example of the **first join**.
Most words on this page contain the
first join.

Copy and write.

a bun and the sun

a vet and a pet

a zip and a chip

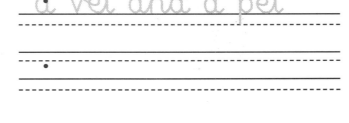

a cap and a map

a bud and some mud

a car and a jar

Name: _____

Remember! There are **four basic joins**.
Most words on this page contain the **first join**.

Copy and write.

I like to hide.

I like to slide.

I like to bake a cake.

I like to dive.

I like to drive.

I like to stay up late!

Name: _____

Remember! There are **four basic joins**.
Here is an example of the **second join**.
Most of the words on this page contain
the second join.

Copy and write.

chicken, cheese and chocolate

a shoe shop, a shark and some sheep

teeth, a thief in a bath and a moth

Name: _____

Remember! There are **four basic joins** in handwriting. Many words on this page contain the **second join**.

Copy and write.

You put rubbish in a sack.

You stick a stamp on a postcard.

You climb a tall beanstalk.

You don't smile at a crocodile!

4

Name: _____

Remember. There are **four basic joins**.
Here is an example of the **third join**.
Most words on this page contain the
third join.

Match the pairs of rhyming words. Write the words.

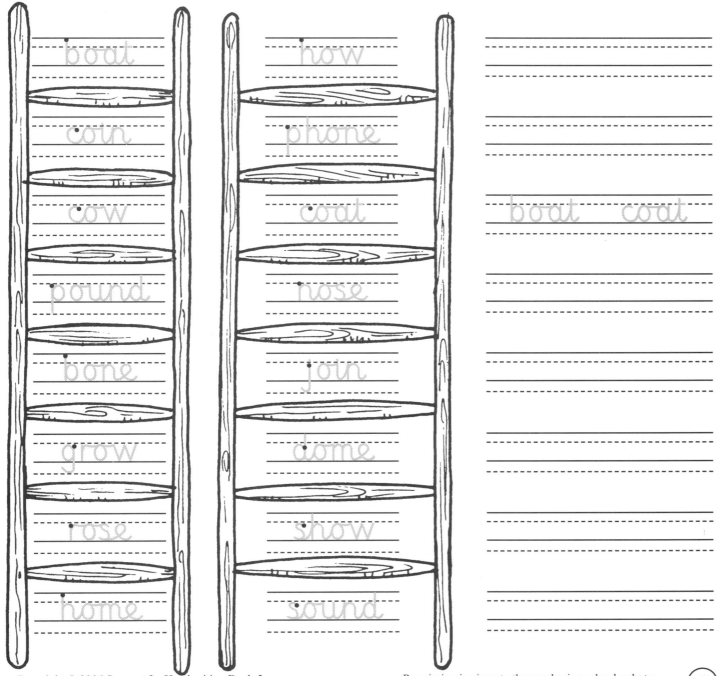

boat   coat

Name: _____

Remember! There are **four basic joins** in handwriting. Many words on this page contain the **third join**.

Copy and write.

There are sixty seconds in one minute.

There are sixty minutes in one hour.

There are twenty-four hours in one day.

There are seven days in one week.

Name: _____

> Remember! There are **four basic joins**.
> Here is an example of the **fourth join**.
> Most words on this page contain
> the fourth join.

Copy and write.

robe   roof   smoke   hote

   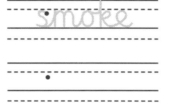

note   sob   office   joke

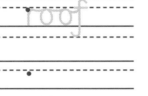 

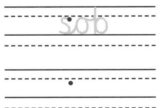 

    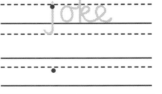

pole   cook   boot   stool

Name: _____

Remember! There are **four basic joins** in handwriting. Many words on this page contain the **fourth join**.

Copy and write.

An owl can fly.

A butterfly can fly.

A flamingo can fly.

A hawk can fly.

A fly can fly, too!

8

Name: _____

Remember! We never make joins after some letters.
These are called **break letters**.
The break letters are: b g j p q x y z

Copy and write.

bread and butter

a piece of pizza

a jar of jam

yummy yogurt

orange squash

sixteen peas

Name: _____

The joins between some letters can be tricky!
You need to practise some of these tricky joins.

Copy and write.

hiss grass stuff sniff

gutter cows cars web

wave feather fence read

Name: _____

Copy and write.

On Monday I felt off my bike.

_____

On Tuesday I had a row with a friend.

_____

On Wednesday the TV blew up!

_____

On Thursday it rained all day.

_____

On Friday I got into trouble at school.

_____

Name: _____

Copy and write.

I would be very pleased if you

would come to the Grand Ball at

the Palace. It will take place on

Saturday 15th September at 8pm.

Please wear your best clothes.

Name: _____

Copy and write.

Anna: Can you fly?

Dragon: All dragons have strong wings.

Anna: Will you take me for a ride?

Dragon: Hop on my back but be careful!

Anna: Ouch! Your scales are prickly!

Dragon: Hold tight! Here we go!

Name: _____

Copy and write.

One day I sat down on a wall. It was

not very safe. I fell off and cracked

my shell. All the king's horses and all

the king's men came along. They tried

to put me together again but they

could not manage to do it.

(14)

Name: _____

Copy and write.

First I wash some potatoes.

Next I peel the potatoes.

Then I cut the potatoes into chips.

Last of all, I fry the chips in hot

oil until they are golden brown.

(15)

Name: _____

Copy and write.

Alice found herself in a long hall.

There were doors all the way round,

but they were locked. How could she

get out? Then Alice saw a little glass

table. On top of it was a gold key.

Name: _____

Copy and write.

An alligator is like a crocodile.

A bat is like a mouse with wings.

A camel lives in the desert.

A dolphin is very intelligent.

An emu cannot fly.

A frog can live on land or in water.

17

Name: _____

Copy and write.

Peg Leg Pete was the most dangerous

pirate in the world. He wore

a spotted scarf on his head.

His bushy eyebrows twitched

like crabs' claws. His eyes

bulged like cannonballs.

Name: _____

Copy and write.

Pandas come from China. They are

rare animals. Pandas are like big

bears. They have round faces, small

ears and a black patch around each

eye. Their thick fur keeps them warm.

19

Name: _____

Copy and write.

What is pink? A rose is pink

By the fountain's brink.

What is red? A poppy's red

In its barley bed.

What is blue? The sky is blue

Where the clouds float through.

Name: _____

Copy and write.

A sea serpent saw a big tanker.

But a hole in her side and sank her.

It swallowed the crew

In a minute or two,

And then picked its teeth with the anchor.

Name: _____

Copy and write.

Animal	Home	Food	When it eats
rabbit	burrow	plants	day or night
badger	set	small animals	at night
fox	den	small animals	at night
squirrel	drey	nuts, bird's eggs	in the day

Copy the chart.

Name: _____

Copy and write.

Jim has headed his last goal.

Tackled his last defender.

Muddied his last pair of shorts.

Cleaned his last pair of boots.

Heard his last cheer from the crowd.

And collected his final red card.

23

Name _____

Name _____   ## Pupil's progress sheet

Page	Letters	Date	Comments
1	The first join (revision 1)		
2	The first join (revision 2)		
3	The second join (revision 1)		
4	The second join (revision 2)		
5	The third join (revision 1)		
6	The third join (revision 2)		
7	The fourth join (revision 1)		
8	The fourth join (revision 2)		
9	Break letters (revision)		
10	Practising tricky letter joins		
11	Practising writing diaries		
12	Practising writing invitations		
13	Practising writing play scripts		
14	Practising writing recounts		
15	Practising writing instructions		
16	Practising writing story beginnings		
17	Practising writing alphabetically-arranged texts		
18	Practising writing descriptions		
19	Practising writing information texts		
20	Practising writing list poems		
21	Practising writing limericks		
22	Practising writing charts		
23	Practising writing epitaphs		